Paper Plate ANIMALS

Reproducible Cut-and-Paste Patterns

Written by
Bee Gee Hazell

Edited by
Kathie Butler

Illustrated by
Lynn Conklin Power

Cover Design by
Joanne Caroselli

Cover Photography by
Rick Gayle

FS-83101 Paper Plate Animals
All rights reserved—Printed in the U.S.A.
Copyright © 1998 Frank Schaffer Publications, Inc.
23740 Hawthorne Boulevard
Torrance, CA 90505

Table of Contents

Getting Started

This book is designed for children and helpers who are interested in making paper plate animals. By completing these projects, children reinforce important skills like listening to directions, finger dexterity, hand-eye coordination, and visual acuity.

Required Materials

- 6-inch white paper plates
- 9-inch white paper plates
- Copy machine
- Copy paper or construction paper
- Scissors
- Glue
- Crayons or markers

Helpful Hints

A. Always make an example of each project before presenting the instructions to children.

B. For the child who is unable to cut intricately, simplify the edges of the pattern pieces.

C. For a more creative effect, various textured materials, bits of colored yarn, fabric, pipe cleaners, and buttons may be glued to the animals.

General Instructions

Paper Plate Animals contains 16 different patterns which are to be photocopied onto paper and used to create 16 different paper plate animals. Both 6-inch and 9-inch paper plates are required for assembling the complete sets of animals. If 6-inch paper plates are hard to find, cut 1 1/2 inches off the edge of a 9-inch paper plate. All of the necessary parts of each animal are in the form of printed patterns for easy duplication on a copy machine. Either copy paper (later to be colored) or colored construction paper may be used. These patterns can also be used as a template on paper. The patterns are colored, cut out, and glued to the paper plates to complete the animals. The instructions call for the patterns to be glued to the plates; however, they can also be stapled to them. Further, we have suggested colors for each animal, but feel free to substitute your own creative color ideas. Detailed directions for each project may be found on pages 6-13.

Project Directions

BIRD

Pattern:
Page 15

Materials:
One 9" white paper plate
One 6" white paper plate
red paper, black paper, yellow paper, scissors, pencil, crayons or markers, glue

Patterns can also be copied onto white paper and colored with crayons or markers.

1. Glue the 6" plate half way down on the right side of the 9" plate. Both plates should face up.

2. Glue wing to the middle of the 9" plate, placing the wing under the 6" plate edge.

3. Glue tail behind the 9" plate above the wing extension.

4. Glue the feet behind the bottom of the 9" plate.

5. Glue beak behind the edge of the 6" plate.

6. Draw an eyeball onto the eye.

7. Glue eye to the middle of the 6" plate.

CAMEL

Pattern:
Page 17 and 18

Materials:
One 9" white paper plate
Two 6" white paper plates
brown paper, black paper, pencil, crayons or markers, scissors, glue

Patterns can also be copied onto white paper and colored with crayons or markers.

1. Cut one 6" plate in half and attach it to the 9" plate to form a camel hump. Use the other 6" plate as the head and the 9" plate as the body. All the plates should face down.

2. Glue the neck edges to the 9" body and 6" head.

3. Glue chin, hair, and ears to the 6" plate.

4. Draw eyes on the head.

5. Glue rear leg, knee, and tail to the body. Add hair to the top of the hump if desired.

Project Directions

CAT

Pattern:
Page 19 and 20

Materials:

One 9" white paper plate
One 6" white paper plate
black paper, blue paper, orange paper, pencil,
crayons or markers, scissors, glue

Patterns can also be copied onto white paper and
colored with crayons or markers.

1. Glue snout to the middle of the 6" plate. This
   plate should be facing up. Before the glue dries,
   place the whiskers under the snout on both sides,
   3 on the left and 3 on the right.

2. Draw eyes on the plate.

3. Glue ears behind the top of the 6" plate.

4. Glue the bow to the bottom of the 6" plate.

5. Glue the 6" plate to the top of the 9" plate. The 9"
   plate should face down.

6. Glue the rear legs on the top left and top right
   sides of the 9" plate.

7. Glue the front legs to the front of the 9" plate.

8. Glue the tail behind the back of the 9" plate on
   the side.

CHICKEN

Pattern:
Page 21

Materials:
One 9" white paper plate
One 6" white paper plate
yellow paper, black paper, red paper, crayons or
markers, pencil, scissors, glue

Patterns can also be copied onto white paper and
colored with crayons or markers.

1. Glue the 6" plate one-third down the right side of
   the 9" plate. Both plates should face up.

2. Glue the comb behind the top of the 6" plate.

3. Glue the beak to the 6" plate.

4. Draw an eyeball on the eye.

5. Glue the eye onto the 6" plate.

6. Glue the wattle under the 6" plate at the chin.

7. Glue the tail feathers to the back of the 9" plate.

8. Glue the wing to the middle of the 9" plate.

9. Glue the feet to the bottom of the legs.

10. Glue the legs to the bottom of the 9" plate.

Project Directions

DOG

Pattern:
Page 23 and 24

Materials:
One 9" white paper plate
One 6" white paper plate
brown paper, pink paper, pencil, crayons or markers, scissors, glue

Patterns can also be copied onto white paper and colored with crayons or markers.

1. Glue the 6" plate one-third down the 9" plate. Both plates should face up.

2. Glue the nose to the middle of the 6" plate.

3. Draw a mouth under the nose.

4. Glue the tongue to the mouth.

5. Draw eyes above the nose.

6. Glue the ears to each side of the 6" plate.

7. Glue rear legs on each side of the 9" plate.

8. Glue the front legs to the front of the plate.

9. Glue the tail behind one of the rear legs.

DUCK

Pattern:
Page 25

Materials:
One 9" white paper plate
One 6" white paper plate
orange paper, scissors, pencil, crayons or markers, glue

Patterns can also be copied onto white paper and colored with crayons or markers.

1. Glue the 6" plate one-third down the left side of the 9" plate. Both plates should face up.

2. Glue the bottom of the beak to the top of the beak.

3. Glue the beak to the 6" plate.

4. Draw an eye on the 6" plate.

5. Place the wing under the edge of the 6" plate and glue it to the 9" plate.

6. Glue the tail to under the back of the 9" plate.

7. Glue the feet under the 9" plate.

Project Directions

COW

Pattern:
Pages 27 and 29

Materials:
One 9" white paper plate
Two 6" white paper plates
black paper, white paper, pencil, scissors, crayons or markers, glue

Patterns can also be copied onto white paper and colored with crayons or markers.

1. Cut straight across a 9" plate 2" from the top. This will be the body. This plate should face down.

2. Glue a 6" plate to the top left of the 9" plate. This will be the head. This plate will face up.

3. Cut the other 6" plate in half. Glue half of the plate, facing up, to the bottom of the 9" plate. This will be the udders.

4. Glue the muzzle to the bottom third of the head.

5. Glue the ears to each side of the head.

6. Glue the horns between the ears so that they curve inside.

7. Draw eyes above the muzzle.

8. Glue the bell under the head.

9. Glue the spots on the body.

10. Glue the tail to the top edge of the body.

11. Glue the legs to the bottom third of the body.

FROG

Pattern:
Page 31 and 32

Materials:
One 9" white paper plate
green paper, white paper, pencil, scissors, crayons or markers, glue

Patterns can also be copied onto white paper and colored with crayons or markers.

1. Draw eyeballs onto the eyes.

2. Glue the eyes to the head.

3. Glue the head one-third down a 9" plate. The plate should face up.

4. Glue the rear legs to each side of the plate.

5. Fold back the front legs along the dotted line. Glue the folded part to the body.

Project Directions

FISH

Pattern:
Page 33

Materials:
One 9" white paper plate
blue paper, pencil, scissors, crayons or markers, glue

Patterns can also be copied onto white paper and colored with crayons or markers.

1. Cut straight across a 9" plate 2" from the top. This will be the body. This plate should face up.

2. Glue the upper fin behind the top of the body.

3. Glue the tail behind the right side of the body.

4. Glue the lower fin behind the bottom of the body.

5. Fold back the gill fin along the dotted line.

6. Glue the folded part of the gill fin to the body.

7. Draw an eyeball on the eye. Glue the eye to the top left of the body.

8. Draw details on the body to represent scales.

9. Draw a mouth on the body under the eyeball.

OWL

Pattern:
Page 35 and 36

Materials:
One 9" white paper plate
One 6" white paper plate
brown paper, pencil, crayons or markers, scissors, glue

Patterns can also be copied onto white paper and colored with crayons or markers.

1. Glue a 6" plate one-third down the 9" plate. Both plates should face up.

2. Glue the brown ear pieces to the middle of the 6" plate so that the tips touch.

3. Draw eyeballs onto the eyes.

4. Glue the eyes onto the ear pieces.

5. Glue the beak to join the face pieces and the eyes.

6. Glue the wings on each side of the 9" plate.

7. Glue the claws to the bottom of the 9" plate.

8. Glue the branch behind the claws.

9. Draw feather details on the 9" plate.

Project Directions

PARROT

Pattern:
Page 37

Materials:
One 9" white paper plate
One 6" white paper plate
blue paper, white paper, black paper, yellow paper, crayons or markers, pencil, scissors, glue

Patterns can also be copied onto white paper and colored with crayons or markers.

1. Glue a 6" plate one-third down a 9" plate. Both plates should face up.

2. Glue beak to the side of the 6" plate.

3. Draw an eyeball on the eye.

4. Glue the eye to the top half of the 6" plate near the beak.

5. Glue the head feathers on top and behind the 6" plate.

6. Glue the wings to each side of the 9" plate.

7. Glue the claws to the bottom of the 9" plate on the top side.

8. Glue the tail feathers behind the claws.

9. Draw feather details on the 9" plate.

PENGUIN

Pattern:
Page 39 and 40

Materials:
One 9" white paper plate
One 6" white paper plate
black paper, orange paper, white paper, crayons or markers, pencil, scissors, glue

Patterns can also be copied onto white paper and colored with crayons or markers.

1. Glue wings on each side of a 9" plate. The plate should face down.

2. Glue the head to the top of the plate.

3. Fold the beak along the dotted line. Glue the beak to the head.

4. Draw eyeballs onto the eyes.

5. Glue the eyes to the head.

6. Glue the feet to the bottom of the plate.

Project Directions

PIG

Pattern:
Page 41

Materials:
One 9" white paper plate
One 6" white paper plate
pink paper, black paper, pencil, crayons or markers, scissors, glue

Patterns can also be copied onto white paper and colored with crayons or markers.

1. Glue a 6" plate one-third down the right side of a 9" plate. Both plates should be facing down.

2. Glue the snout to the 6" plate.

3. Draw eyes onto the 6" plate.

4. Fold the ears down along the dotted line. Glue the ears behind the top of the 6" plate.

5. Cut the tail along the dotted line.

6. Glue the tail behind the side of the 9" plate.

7. Glue the feet to the inside bottom of the 9" plate.

RABBIT

Pattern:
Page 43

Materials:
One 9" white paper plate
One 6" white paper plate
pink paper, white paper, yellow paper, black paper, crayons or markers, pencil, scissors, glue

Patterns can also be copied onto white paper and colored with crayons or markers.

1. Glue the 6" plate one-third down the 9" plate. Both plates should face up.

2. Glue the inner ears to the outer ears.

3. Glue ears behind the top of the 6" plate.

4. Glue the cheek to the 6" plate.

5. Glue the nose to the top center of the cheek. Before the glue dries, place the whiskers under the cheek on both sides, 3 on the left and 3 on the right.

6. Draw eyes above the nose.

7. Glue two paws to the front of the 9" plate.

8. Glue two paws to the bottom of the 9" plate.

9. Glue the tail to the bottom side of the 9" plate.

Project Directions

SHEEP

Pattern:
Page 45 and 46

Materials:
One 9" white paper plate
One 6" white paper plate
black paper, white paper, scissors, pencil, crayons or markers, glue

Patterns can also be copied onto white paper and colored with crayons or markers.

1. Glue the 6" plate, facing up, one-third down the right side of the 9" plate. The 9" plate should face down.

2. Draw eyes on the face.

3. Glue the face to the 6" plate with the bottom of the face lining the bottom of the plate.

4. Glue the ears to the top side of the 6" plate.

5. Glue the bell under the 6" plate.

6. Glue the feet under the bottom of the 9" plate.

7. Glue the tail under the side of the 9" plate.

TURKEY

Pattern:
Page 47

Materials:
Two 9" white paper plates
One 6" white paper plate
brown paper, yellow paper, red paper, crayons or markers, pencil, scissors, glue

Patterns can also be copied onto white paper and colored with crayons or markers.

1. Glue the 6" plate down the left side of a 9" plate. All plates should face up.

2. Cut the other 9" plate in half. Cut slits into the ends to form feathers.

3. Glue the beak onto the 6" plate.

4. Glue the wattle on top of the beak so it hangs below.

5. Draw an eyeball onto the eye.

6. Glue the eye onto the 6" plate.

7. Place the end of the wing under the 6" plate and glue. Place the end of the feathers under the wing and glue.

8. Glue the feet behind the bottom of the 9" plate.

Directions on page 6.

Cut (1)
wing

Cut (2)
feet

Cut (1)
eye

Cut (1)
beak

Cut (1) tail

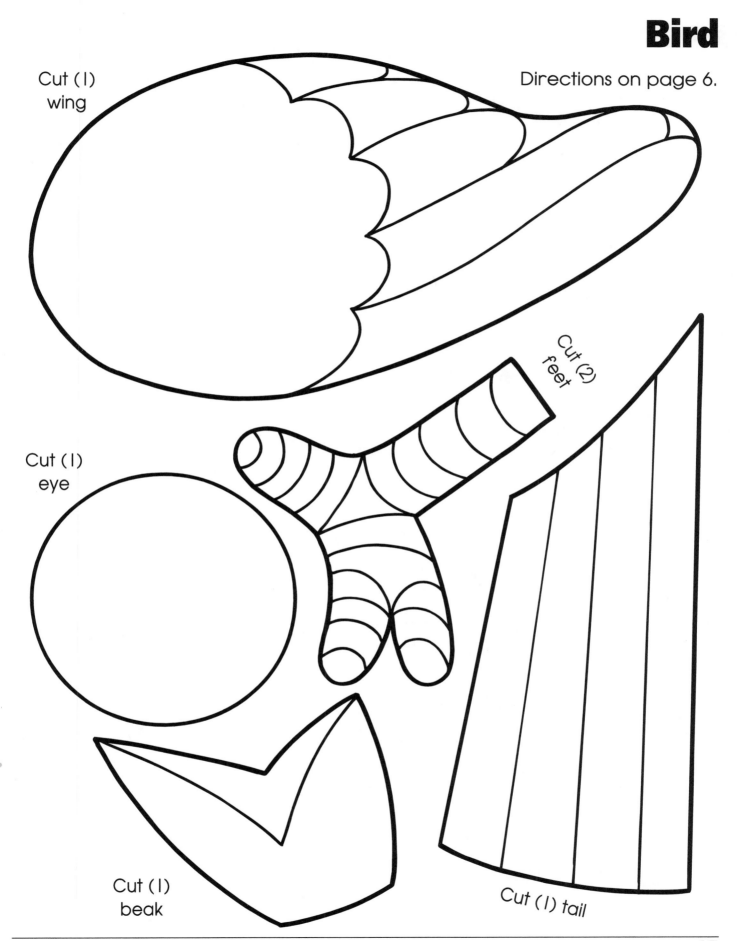

Camel

Cut (1) neck

top

bottom

Cut (1) knee

Cut (2) ears

Cut (2) legs

Cut (1) chin

Camel

Directions on page 6.

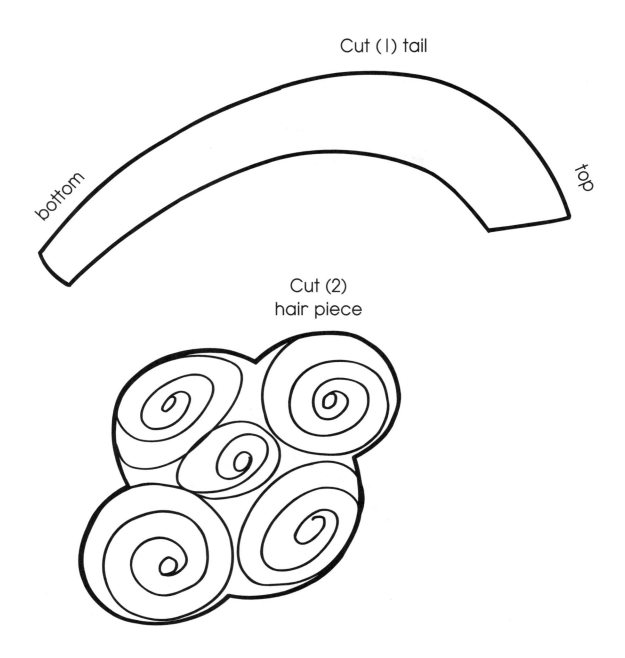

Cut (1) tail

bottom

top

Cut (2)
hair piece

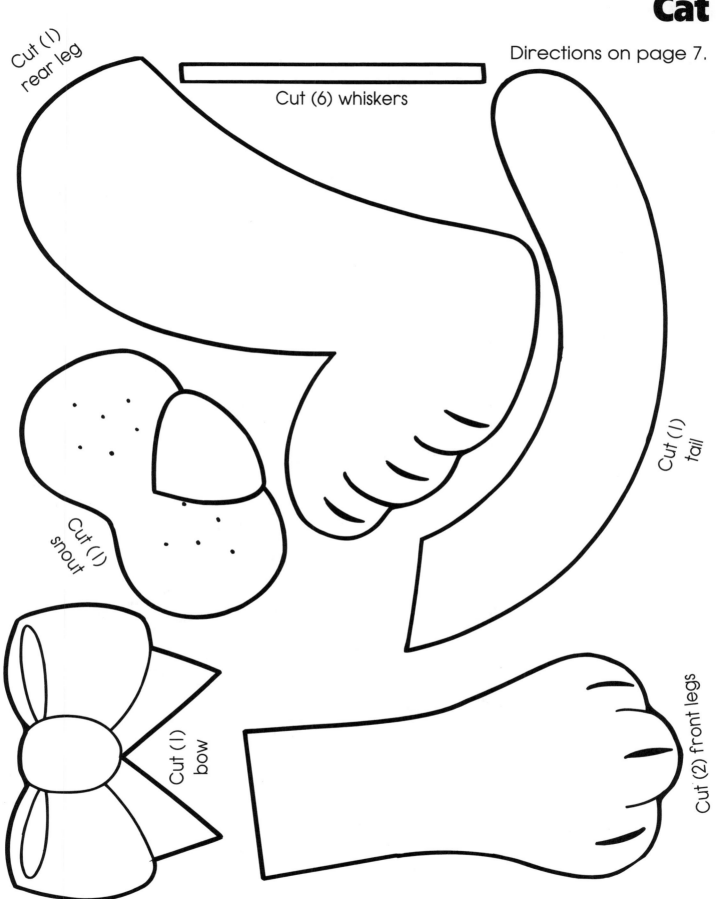

Cut (1)
rear leg

Cut (6) whiskers

Directions on page 7.

Cut (1)
tail

Cut (1)
snout

Cut (1)
bow

Cut (2) front legs

Cat

Directions on page 7.

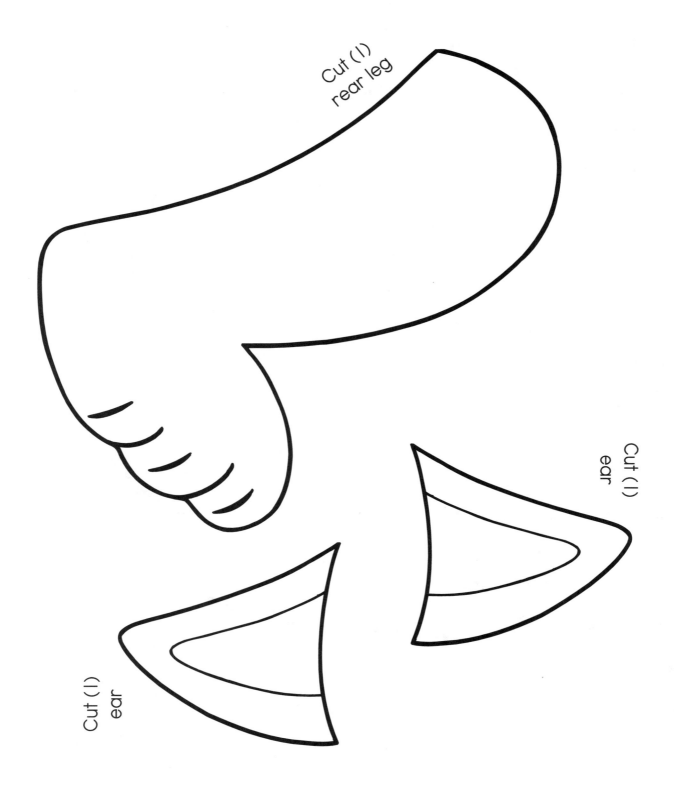

Cut (1)
rear leg

Cut (1)
ear

Cut (1)
ear

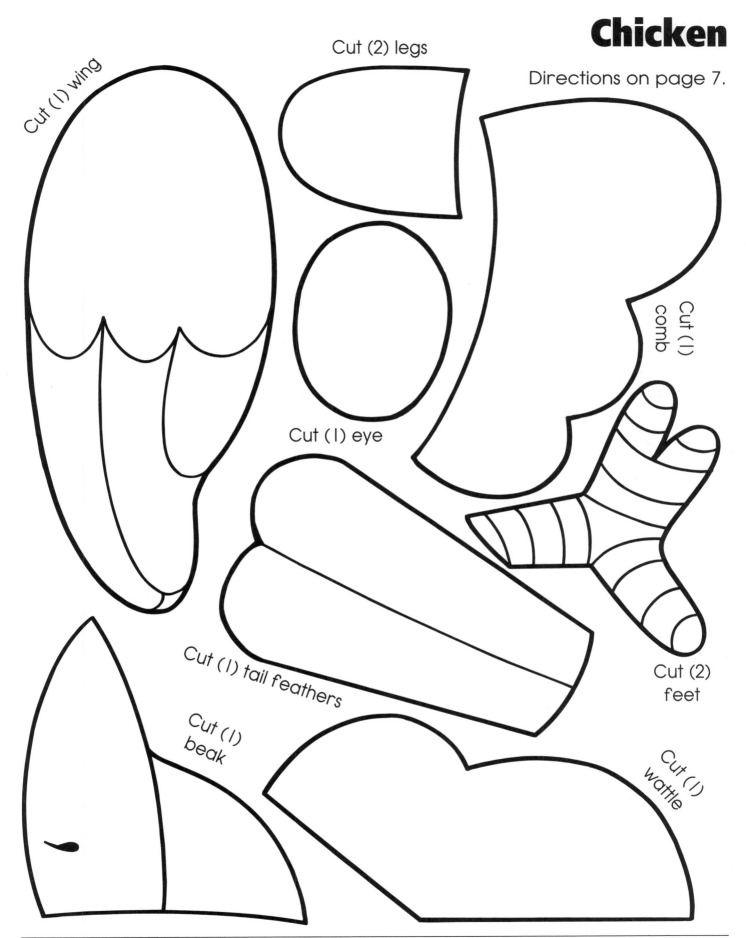

Chicken

Directions on page 7.

Cut (1) wing

Cut (2) legs

Cut (1) comb

Cut (1) eye

Cut (1) tail feathers

Cut (2) feet

Cut (1) beak

Cut (1) wattle

Directions on page 8.

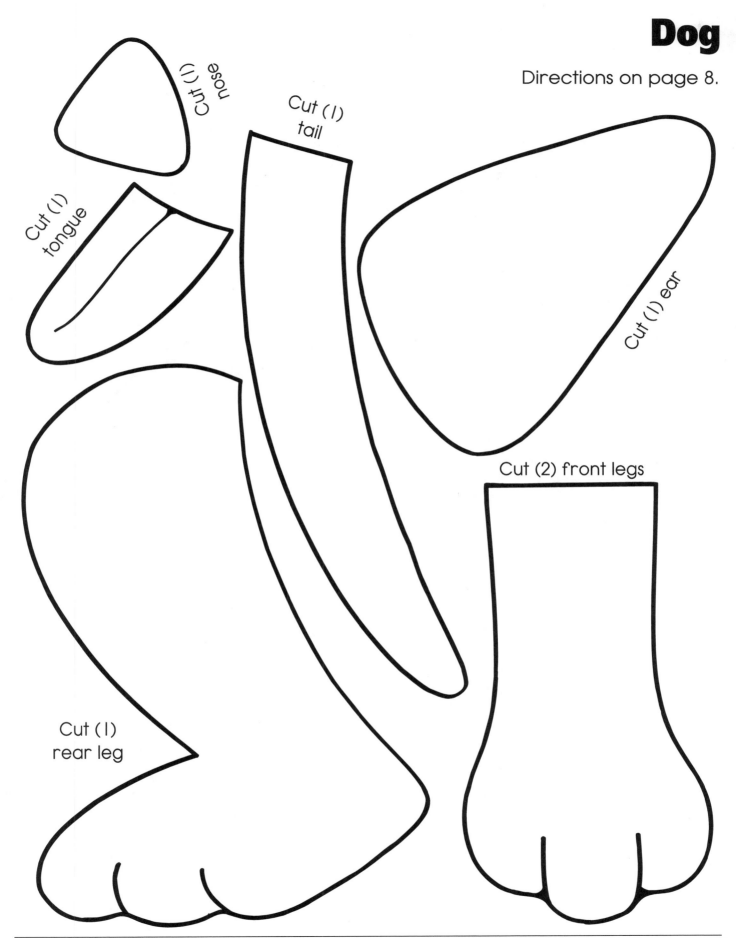

Cut (1) nose

Cut (1) tongue

Cut (1) tail

Cut (1) ear

Cut (2) front legs

Cut (1) rear leg

Dog

Directions on page 8.

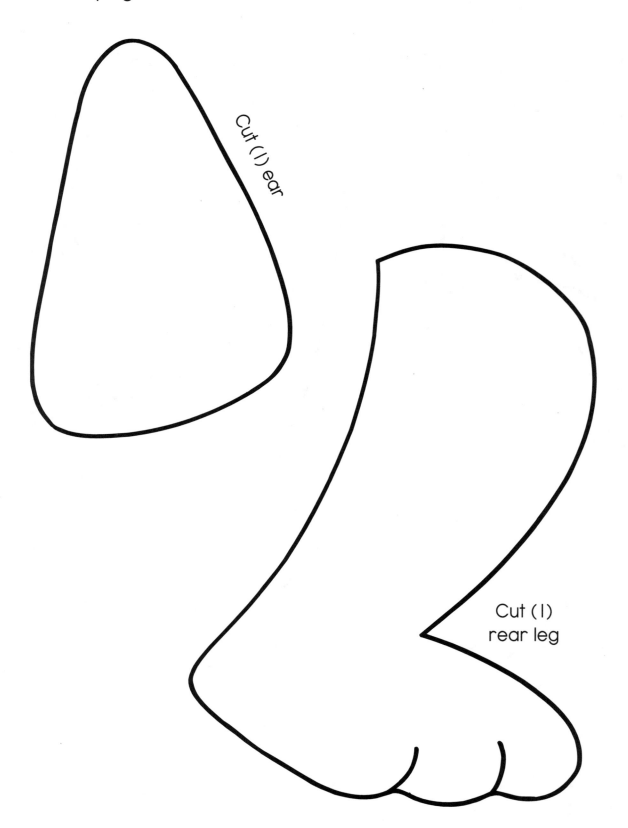

Cut (1) ear

Cut (1)
rear leg

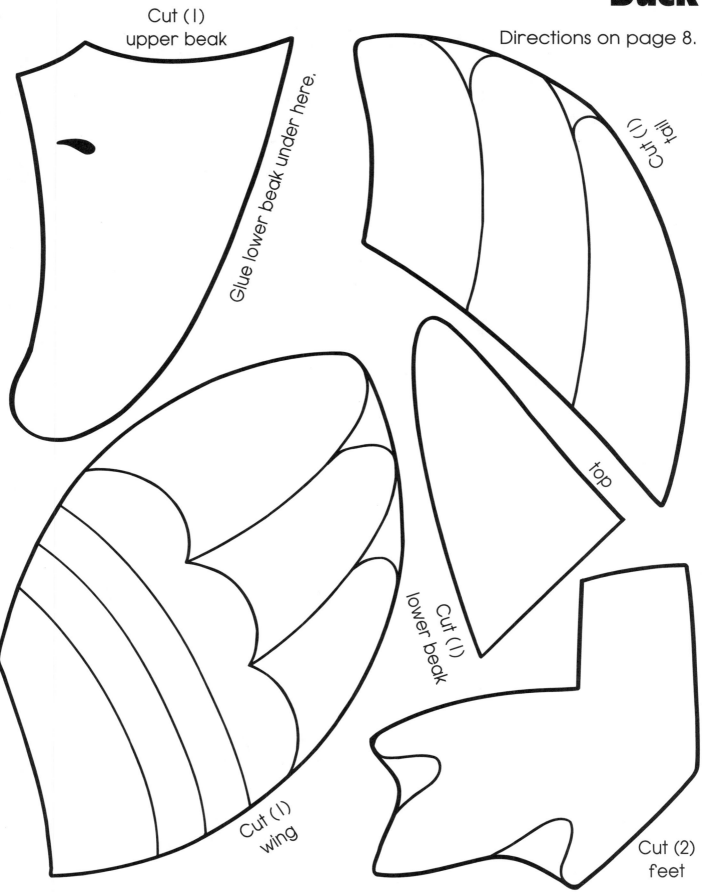

Duck

Directions on page 8.

Cut (1)
upper beak

Glue lower beak under here.

Cut (1)
tail

top

Cut (1)
lower beak

Cut (1)
wing

Cut (2)
feet

Directions on page 9.

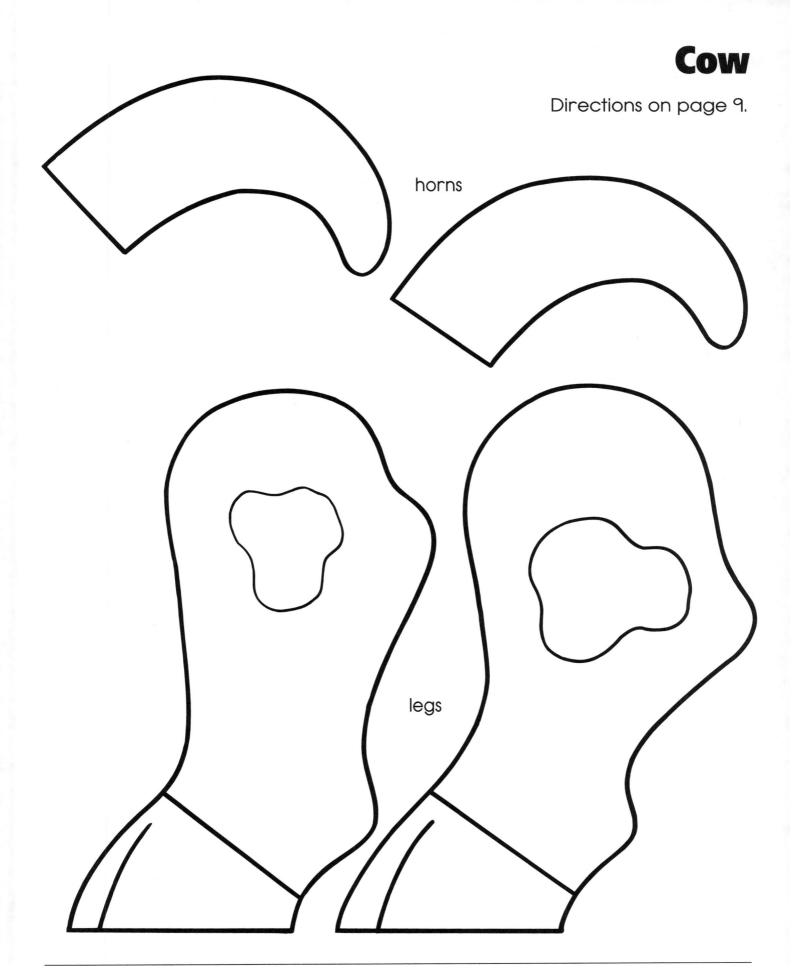

horns

legs

Cow

Directions on page 9.

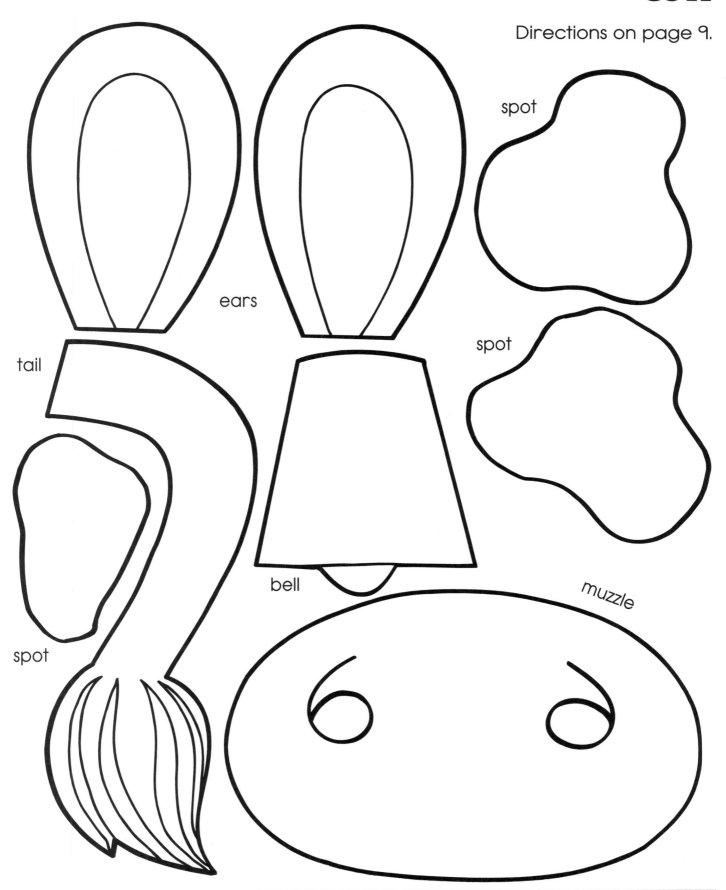

spot

ears

spot

tail

bell

muzzle

spot

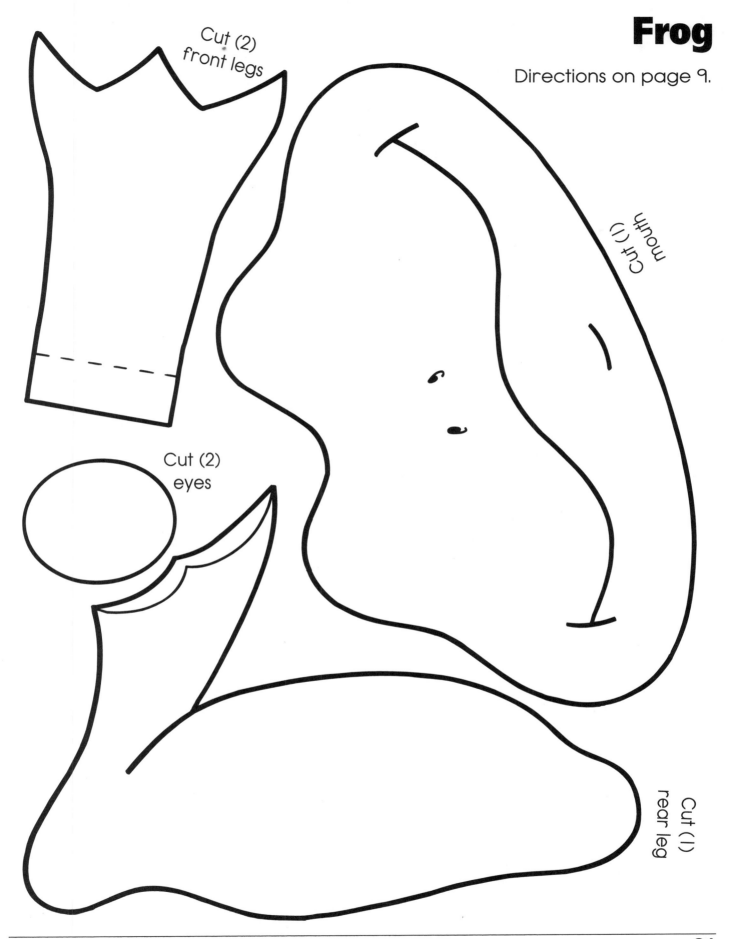

Cut (2)
front legs

Frog

Directions on page 9.

Cut (1)
mouth

Cut (2)
eyes

Cut (1)
rear leg

Frog

Directions on page 9.

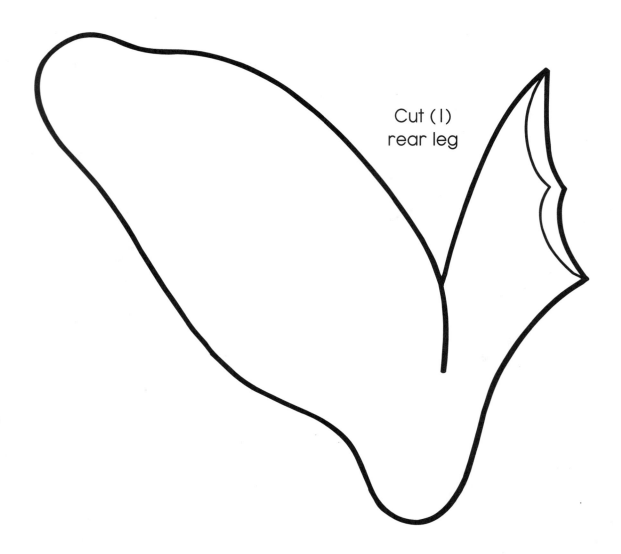

Cut (1)
rear leg

upper fin

Directions on page 10.

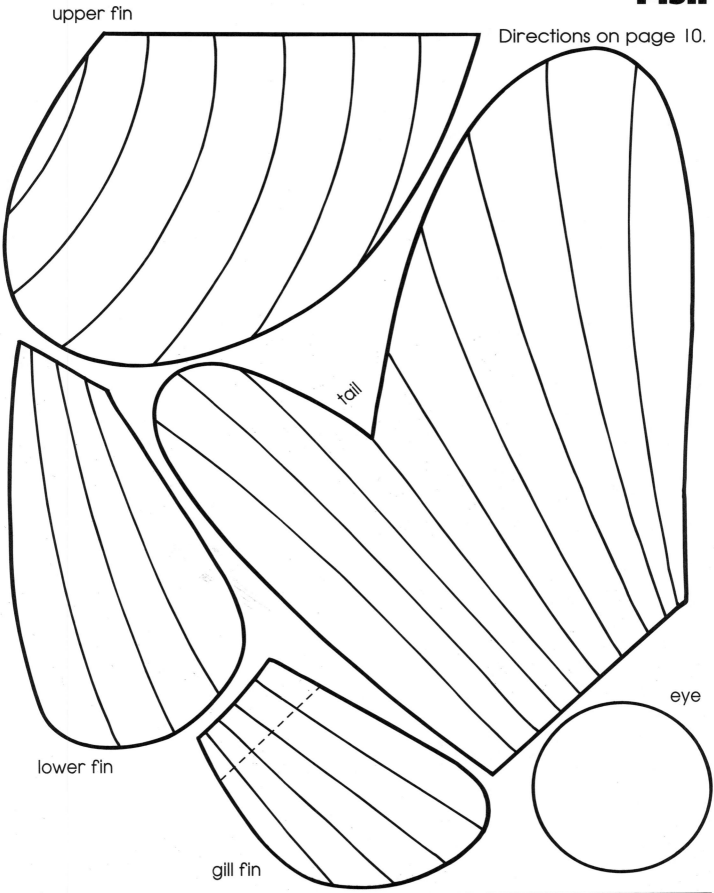

tail

eye

lower fin

gill fin

Owl

Directions on page 10.

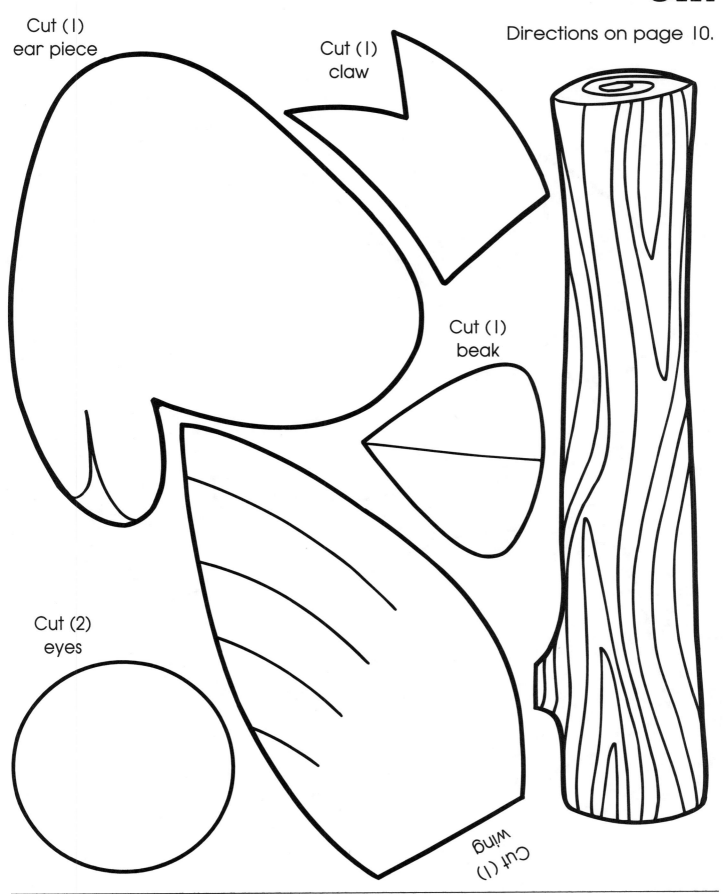

Cut (1)
ear piece

Cut (1)
claw

Cut (1)
beak

Cut (2)
eyes

Cut (1)
wing

Owl

Directions on page 10.

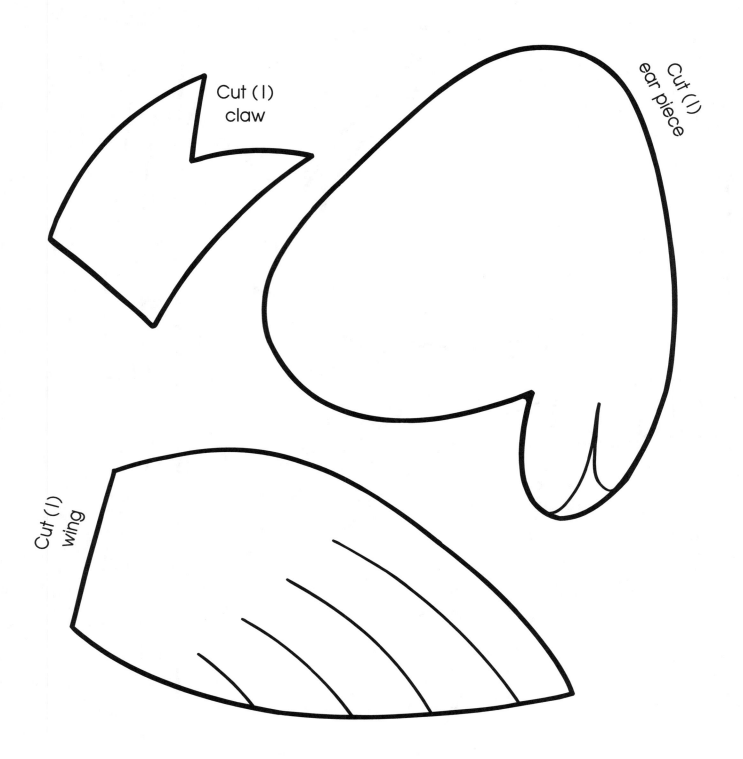

Cut (1)
claw

Cut (1)
ear piece

Cut (1)
wing

Parrot

Directions on page 11.

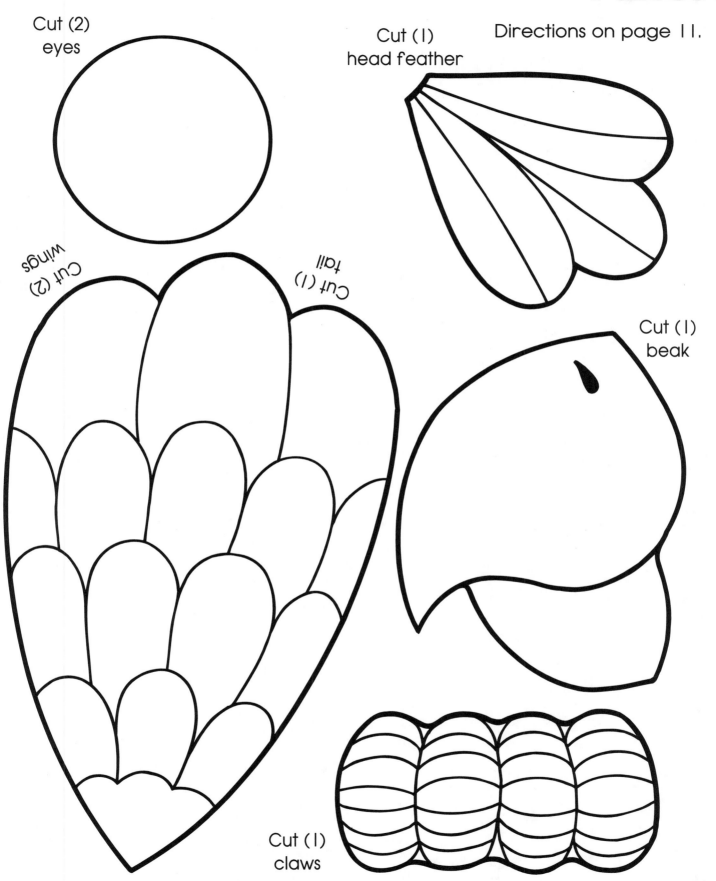

Cut (2)
eyes

Cut (1)
head feather

Cut (2)
wings

Cut (1)
tail

Cut (1)
beak

Cut (1)
claws

Penguin

Directions on page 11.

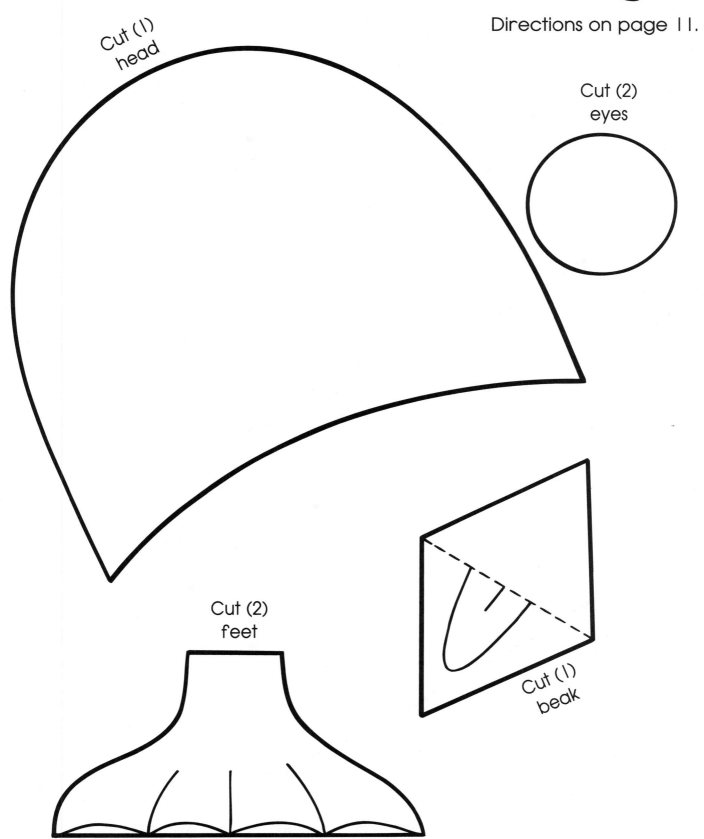

Cut (1)
head

Cut (2)
eyes

Cut (2)
feet

Cut (1)
beak

Penguin

Directions on page 11.

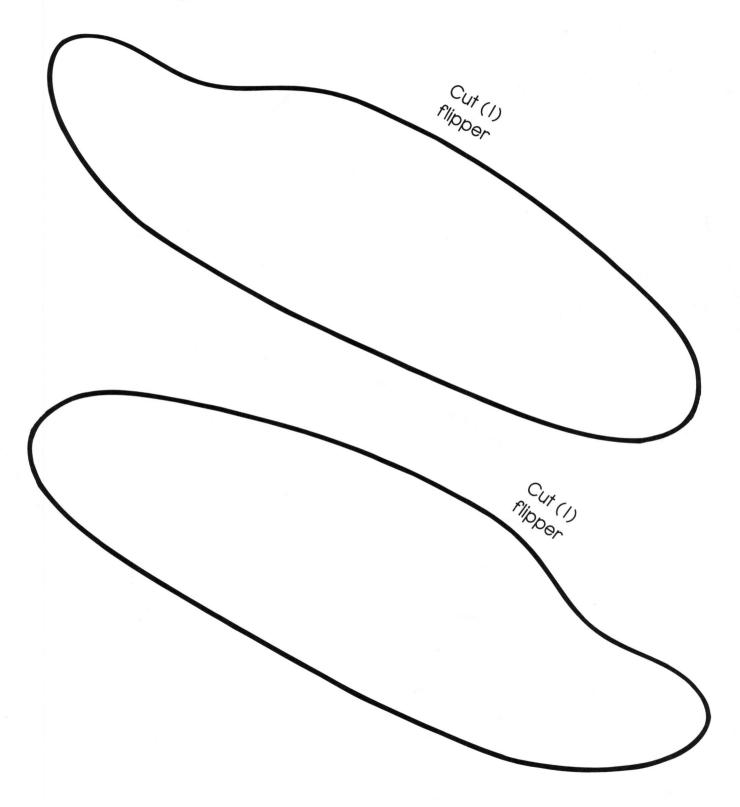

Cut (1)
flipper

Cut (1)
flipper

Directions on page 12.

Cut (2)
ears

Cut (2)
feet

Cut (1)
snout

Cut

Cut (1) tail

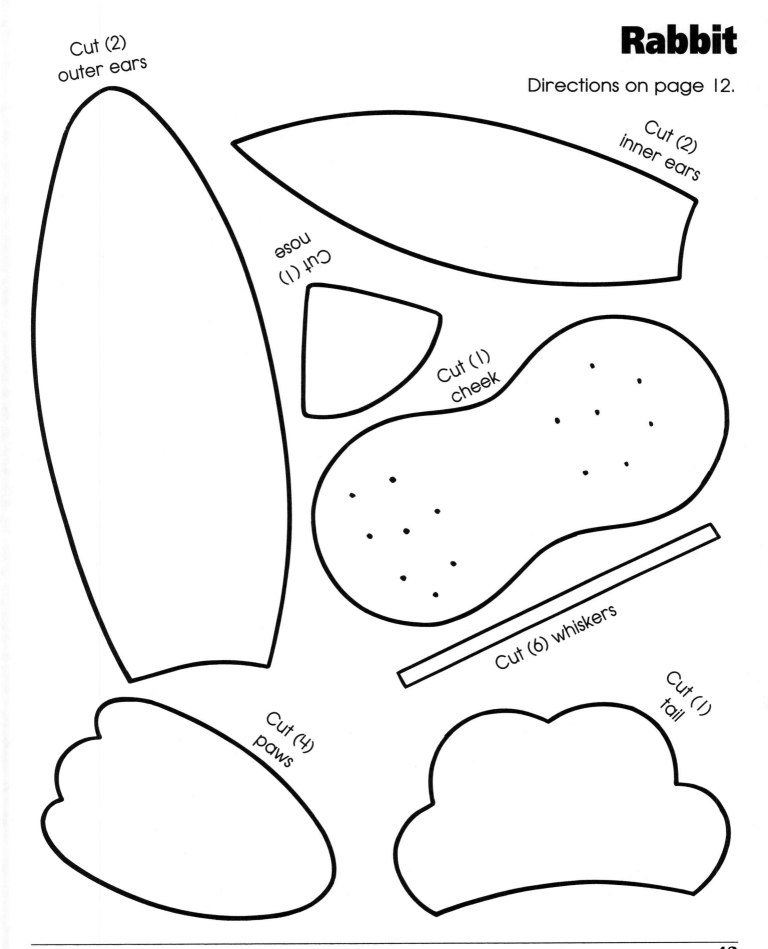

Rabbit

Directions on page 12.

Cut (2)
outer ears

Cut (2)
inner ears

Cut (1)
nose

Cut (1)
cheek

Cut (6) whiskers

Cut (4)
paws

Cut (1)
tail

Sheep

Directions on page 13.

Cut (1)
face

Cut (1)
tail

Cut (1)
wool

Sheep

Directions on page 13.

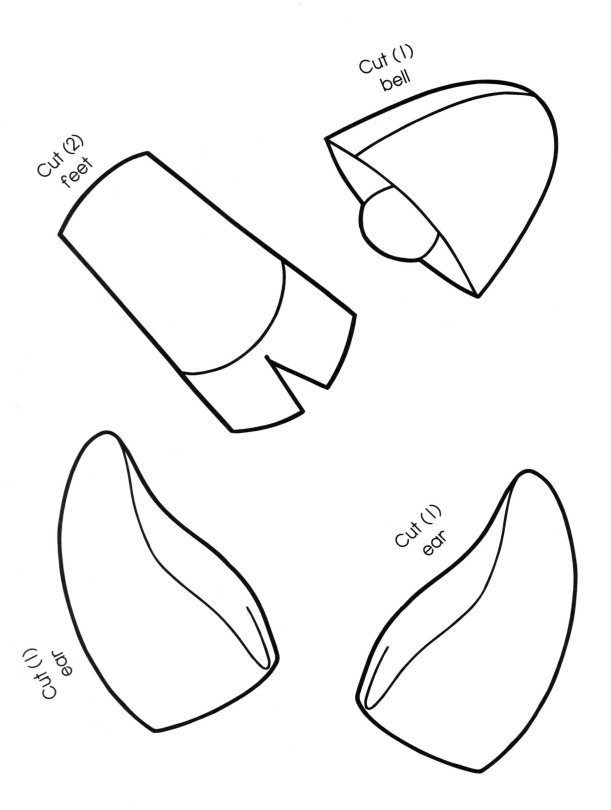

Cut (1)
bell

Cut (2)
feet

Cut (1)
ear

Cut (1)
ear

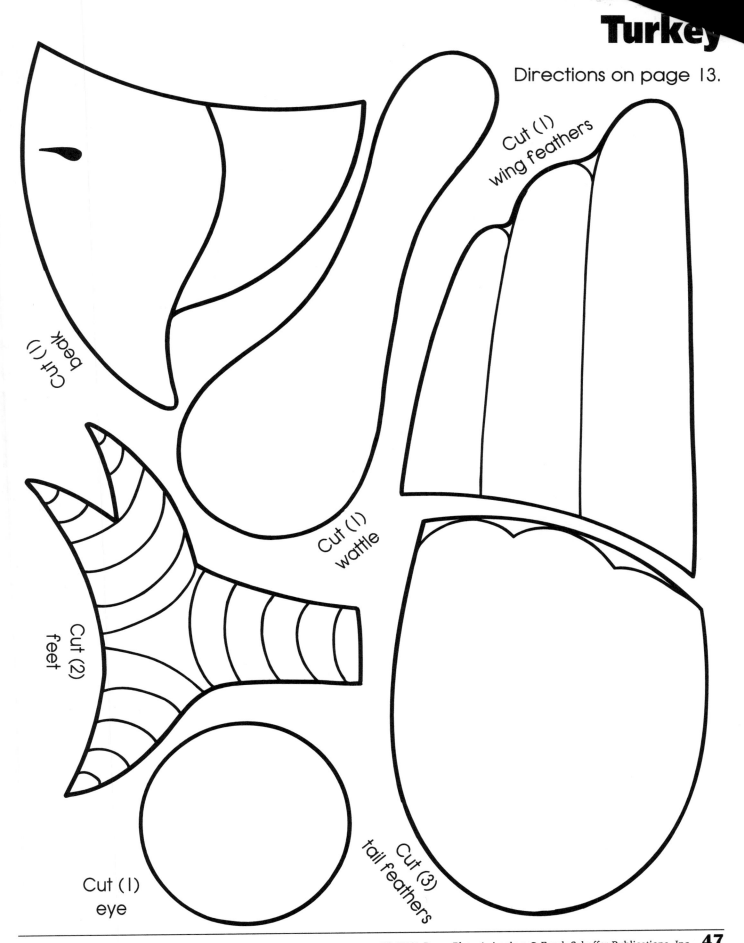

Directions on page 13.

Cut (1)
wing feathers

Cut (1)
beak

Cut (1)
wattle

Cut (2)
feet

Cut (3)
tail feathers

Cut (1)
eye